ROBE
Hi

Robert Hull was brought up in Lancashire, and
educated at grammar school and Cambridge. He went
to Canada as a shool-teacher, and there met his wife.
They settled in Sussex and had two children, who now
have their own. After twenty-odd years of school-
teaching, he worked for some time on university
literature and writing courses. He now works freelance,
and visits schools to run workshops, and writes, and
whenever he can explores the coast and lanes of Sussex
on his bike.

Also by Robert Hull

POETRY FOR CHILDREN
Stargrazer (Hodder 1997) — shortlisted for the
Signal prize
Everest and Chips (Oxford University Press 2002) —
shortlisted for the CLPE prize

POETRY FOR ADULTS
Encouraging Shakespeare (Peterloo 1993)
On Portsmouth Station (Beafred 2008)

FICTION
West African Stories (Wayland 1998) — shortlisted for
the 1999 Kurt Maschler Award

FOR TEACHERS
Behind the Poem (Routledge 1988)
*Poetry — from Reading to Writing —
A Classroom Guide for Ages 7–11* (Routledge 2009)

ROBERT HULL

High Tide

❖

Children's Poetry Library
No. 7

SALT

London

PUBLISHED BY SALT PUBLISHING
Fourth Floor, 2 Tavistock Place, Bloomsbury,
London WC1H 9RA United Kingdom

© Robert Hull, 2010

The right of Robert Hull to be identified as the
editor of this work has been asserted by him in accordance
with Section 77 of the Copyright, Designs and Patents Act 1988.

First published 2010

Printed in the UK by the MPG Books Group

Typeset in Oneleigh 11/14

ISBN 978 1 84471 506 0 paperback

1 3 5 7 9 8 6 4 2

to Jan

CONTENTS

ACKNOWLEDGEMENTS

'Shadows, Deer's Skull' and 'Hunting in February' appeared previously in *Stargrazer* (Hodder 1997) 'Space', 'Beginnings', 'English Rules', 'Peace Process' and 'Things with Feathers', appeared in *Everest and Chips* (OUP 2002)

SPACE

On a sphere of blue
marbled with white
taking a trip
through silent night,

out for a spin
in starry space
go me and you
and the human race.

BLACK HOLE

Light bends, gets pulled around
like elastic.

I can get that.

But trying to think
of light trying to escape from somewhere
and being pulled back
faster than it can travel —

the idea's beyond me.

Whenever I try to see that,
my thoughts just don't get out
into the light —

my imagination
gets hauled back into a sort of
black hole in my head.

THE MAKER SAID,

'My next creature
will make urgent
leaps across grass

and ripple itself
low to the leaves
and run his back along
branches like an artist
outlining them
with a quick pencil

and perform fine
flourishes of tail —

her high-speed paws
will rotate apple cores
and rain bits everywhere

or be held thoughtfully
at the breast as if in prayer
before they open
in an *oh my!*
of wonder
at the world she's in.'

BEGINNINGS

Perhaps all this

was shouted into being
by the sudden anger
of thunder

or sky
whet her fingers
in sprawled lakes
and sang the winds
across a flute

or the tree
of dark fell
and levered out
a root-face of white rock

or a frog
climbed to the top
of the pond of dark
and gulped out light

or from the wall
of silence
trailed shining
cranesbill

or the newt
hiding dawn
under its belly
banked upwards
with spread hands

or a thrush
broke open the shell
where light coiled

or all of this
this morning.

SNOW

And now there's not much left to go
of all that swirling driving snow

that fell for days and made our row
of white-roofed houses shine and glow
as bright as Alps, a week ago.

It soon slid free down wet slates
and showered from eaves and slipped off gates
and gutters ran small glinting spates

of water melted from the snow
that lit our street just days ago.

MY COLOURED PENS

White
is for things like bright
angels, snow,
and polite
thank-you letters.

Green's
for grassy scenes,
and scribbling my head off
about nature and stuff.

I'll use blue
for what's crazy
but true about you,

and save gold
for a card to someone
ninety years old.

Black's for in stories
when aliens attack,
also the pain
in dad's back,

and grey
for what teachers say
day after day
after day.

Red's
for rusty sheds
and poppy-heads
and wrong words
I've said,

and pink
for a Valentine
so crazy with roses
it'll make you blink.

Yellow
fits a monster's bellow
and the man next door
torturing his cello,

then I can use magenta or puce
for crossing out
anything in this
that's no use.

OUR SHORT BUT INTERESTING GREEK BUS JOURNEY

The first thing was passengers watching
dad trying to wrestle down
our dripping Lilo
that kept writhing up straight

then we had to stop
right at the edge of the harbour
while an old man drinking coffee
moved his chair

then a young woman got off
the driver must have fancied
because he tried a kind of caress
with the side of the bus

then a little girl was sick
into a plastic bag and her mum
wound the window down
and threw it out

then a lady got on
with two loud chickens
then suddenly we arrived
unfortunately.

HUNTING IN FEBRUARY

I'm hunting this morning
with the eye and the ear
not the gun.
I'm out to catch the sun

in icy ditches.
I'm tracking two nuthatches
avoiding me
tree after tree.

I peer in each pond,
scan each path
for signs
of wakening earth.

I watch on a fence-post
a dozing hawk
ignoring a crow's
scold and scrawk,

hear frogs creak
their old hosannas
from the melting pond's
slimy saunas,

catch a glimpse
at the Rother's edge
of grayling sunning
under Shopham bridge.

Eye and ear
are the gear to use
for throwing over creatures
the mind's noose.

You'll only ever
hold in the heart's
keepnet the glitter
of sudden kingfisher,

or the clear glance
the fox gives you
paused at the lane's
edge in rain;

you need no weapon
to bag a fine pheasant
or stalk the heron
at the pond's rim,

or snare the shadows
clouds pull
across the fields
under Duncton Hill.

MR FROG,

what are doing here
on our kitchen floor?

It's not that you aren't welcome,
it's nice to see you here,
but on a sunny morning like this

shouldn't you be hanging around
with your friends in the pond
sunning and dozing?

You don't look a bit at home
down there either,
flopped under that chair,

a veil of misty stuff
round your lower half
like mould or dandruff.

I could rinse it off,
give you a gentle spray,
but you'd hop away

in alarm.
And the dew on the lawn
is fresher, cooler —

let me take you there.

DEER'S SKULL

This awkward chalky latch
must have been what flicked the ears
this way and that,

this snapped biro-end of bone
the thin corridor
that sounds of the fields crowded down.

To think these dusty caves of muzzle
were once aswirl
with the woods' faint scents,

that under this brain's thin
meander of suture, suns rose
and stars fell.

I wonder when it last stared
across the hot whisper of this wheat field
watching someone watching.

SHADOWS

Lovely the shadows
of gulls at rest on the water

of trout hovering over sunlit gravel
in the river

of the oak at sunset
lengthening down the hill.

Different the shadows

that darken the chart

fill the window

stop the heart.

FROST

Frost the jailer
locks each ditch
and pool and pond
and slams the door
on moving water.

Frost the jeweller
fingers each gem
at the leaf's tip
keen to account
for every drip.

Frost the miser
hoards the silver
leaves of winter
in dark hollows
under beech and poplar.

Frost the odd-job man
does up the garden
renewing each post
and leaning fence
at minimum cost.

Frost the magician
binds the day
in a silver spell
draping in white
fold and fell.

Frost the old man
who might not see April
taps with his white
stick in the garden
not feeling right.

'PLEASE DO NOT FEED THE ANIMALS . . .'

Please do not feed the ostriches
sandwiches

or the polar bears
éclairs.

Do not offer the wombats
kumquats

or the rattle-snakes
fruit-cakes.

Remember that piranhas
are not allowed bananas

or partridges
sausages.

Never approach a stork
with things on a fork

or the bustard
with a plate of custard.

No leopard
likes anything peppered

and meerkats
dislike Kit Kats.

Remember that grapes
upset apes

and meringues
do the same for orang-utans.

Most importantly —
do not feed the cheetah

your teacher.

STARTING SCHOOL — PRESTON, 1912

At the interview for the girls' grammar school,
when you told the Headmistress you wanted to be a
      teacher,
she nodded and smiled; she approved wholeheartedly
of the profession of School-Teaching, she said,
though most of her girls were being trained
to take their place in society as ladies.

To your father, who'd had taken the day off from the
      factory,
she seemed like a sort of duchess.
And two pounds a term was a lot, he said
      afterwards —
he'd have to think about it.

But you went. The neighbours helped. They donated
a second-hand gym slip, and a straw boater
with a Park School hat-band ten years old.
You said it was shabby, and felt embarrassed
the first morning as you walked on your own
down Fishergate from the station.

And without knowing, you were already breaking
a school rule: you weren't wearing gloves.

You spent the whole of your first morning thinking
the girls were staring at you and saying things,
but a week later you'd come first in arithmetic,
and found you played the piano better
then the beauty who taught dancing.

But it *was* a school for ladies. Once in assembly
the Headmistress announced that two girls
— in school uniform, *and* not wearing gloves —
had been seen dropping toffee-papers
from the upper deck of a tram-car
on the driver's head below!

You only stayed two years there.
You remembered it happily — you'd some nice friends.
But you never came higher than eighth in the form,
so you couldn't teach, your father said,
and two pounds a term was still a lot.

The day you left, your form mistress walked with you
round the tennis-court, saying how surprised she was
you were leaving, and sorry — you'd been
such a help to her. You wondered how,
as you walked on your own
down Fishergate to the train,
aged just fourteen.

'SCARY DOESN'T HAVE AN E, JAMES.'

But Miss I want *scary* to have an *e*
because *scarey* with an *e* sounds more scarey
than *scary*.

Don't be silly James.

Miss don't you think an apple pie's
tastier if it's *appley*
than if it's *apply?*

No I certainly don't James.

But Miss, the *e*'s
look right in these — look, here —
adjective thingies.

Not 'adjective thingies' — adjectives.

I've got some more here, Miss.
Doesn't it make a snake sound snakier
to say it's *snakey* instead *of snaky ?*
and scalier if it's *scaley* not *scaly ?*

No it most certainly doesn't, James.
It doesn't make any difference,
it's just wrong.

Like snow-flakes would look flakier
if they were *flakey*
and lakes would be lakier
if they were *lakey*.

That's all very silly, James.

Miss you have to be more tolerant
and open to change and difference.
And it's not all as straightforward
as you think — for instance
a cemetery may be *holy* with no *e*
but you have to admit it's very *holey*
not to mention *moley*.

You're wasting your time and mine James.
Words are spelled one way and that's that.

Ok — and by the way Miss,
my name's not *James*
it's *Jamey*, with an *e*.

ENGLISH RULES — 'DON'T USE "AND" ALL THE TIME'

But I like *and*
I'm a fan.

Without *and*
where would here and now be
and yes and no
and you and me?

Without *and*
the knife wouldn't have a fork to eat with
and the burger would have had its chips.

And adds to life
it's a more-of-where-that-came-from,
a sunny plus,
not a misty minus.

And and and
keeps stories chugging along
like a little engine.

Without *and*
no one could be the life and soul of the party
the bible would collapse
and the egg couldn't bring home the bacon.

Ripe conkers are *and*
and second helpings
and extra time

And big sloppy dogs
and daft jokes
and love
and the genius you'll be tomorrow.

And . . .

SLOVENLY STUDENT, 1345

December. Misty ice
across library glass.
His nose runs,
he can't be bothered
to wipe it before it drips
its dew on the page.
He marks the passages
he wants to read again
by skreaking a long coal-black
finger-nail down the side of the page.
He leaves stems of straw in the pages
so he can find them again —
the book fattens
till its clasps ache.
He stops for lunch.
As he whispers to his mates,
bits of fruit and cheese and saliva
flick down over the book.
Afterwards, he dozes,
leaning his head down
on the half-turned page,
creasing it, and dreams
of a great future.

RECENT HISTORY LESSON

Men with shells
versus women with shopping

a mortar
versus a market

a tank
versus a nursery

orders
versus toddlers

soldiers with maps
versus people with nowhere.

PEACE PROCESS

Things are finally moving,
a spokesperson says.

Even now officials
are on their knees measuring

the huge handshake
the leaders did up there,

while specialists scrutinise
the innards of smiles.

It appears the leaders
may have been alone long enough

to consummate a sentence,
which could mean that the people

may yet be permitted
not to run out of future.

PING FENG

is a Chinese pig
with a human head

at each end. Ping Feng
is always in two minds,

and two moods,
like a tram

that doesn't know
which way to go.

One end's fascinated
when the other's bored,

one end's cheery
if the other's grumpy,

one end's hopeful,
the other's given up.

One end likes chips
the other cabbage,

one end's into books
the other watches telly,

one end likes ping-pong
the other mah-jong.

But they don't quarrel,
they only differ.

In fact Ping Feng's
two ends

(this could be the moral)
are best friends.

FROGS

This year, for some reason,
they've not come back —
the thirty-odd frogs
that populated
our five-foot pond.

We haven't heard them
from moorings
of leaf and stone slipping
under in numbers
when unstealthily
approached,

or in noon sun
seen a henge of heads
glistening like pen-nibs
or the corners
of foundered crisp-bags.

Camouflaged green
they'd doze on low alert
on iris leaves,
or jut skywards,
mimicking in the pond's
algal silos,
missiles threatening.

They'd sit up smart
in the rain,
and emigrate
in too much heat
to waste and wet.

We miss their farthing-
sized offspring swaying
like stranded pole-vaulters
on the tips of grass-blades,
their low motor-bike-like voices
in spring rain.

CAT SISTERS

For fifteen years
the way they lay by fires
warmed us,
the way they wandered upstairs
winter and summer
mewing at the morning
lit the sun's way in.
They'd agitate our sluggish days,
their cries for sustenance
making rising easier,
and in extreme need might place
a considerate paw
on the cheek of a sleeping face.
Now they no longer
make holidays more anxious,
staying over a problem,
their yawns, their dreams, their games,
their ills, their hurts as far
gone from these rooms
as their swept fur,
lying together
under the darkening ash
of their fifteenth summer.

TABLE

We were going to sell the table.
It's big where it is,
with those elbowing edges
coming after us
and corners
that force us into corners.

But we decided not to. Instead,
we said,
we'd rub down the surface,
get rid of each burn and dent
and moon of stain
and the stuck inch of newsprint.

But we've not even been able
to start cleaning our old table.

It's had too many babies
changed on it,
too many trumpets
and spoons whanged on it,
too many whales and witches
drawn on it
to do anything with it;

there's been too much homework and grief
dumped on it, too much laughter
heard round it, too many candles
burned down over it,
to do anything else but leave it there,
in the awkward place it's in,

elbowing us with its edges,
reminding us.

SORRY, MOUSE

We're concerned for you,
small mouse,
twisting and turning
in your plastic safe-house,
deprived of even
the bit of cheese
that lured you in.

So now seems the time —
while both cats dream
oblivious by the fire,
tired of waiting for you
to stir from behind the cooker —
to take and gently
empty you
to long grass
at the waste end
of our garden —

and for exiling you
from this warm
but dangerous
(for a mouse)
house,

beg your pardon.

THINGS WITH FEATHERS

"Hope" is the thing with feathers
That perches in the soul
                    —EMILY DICKINSON

Give us a tune, thing with feathers —
sing it in all weathers.

Sing it for eagle, osprey, wren,
kite, owl, sparrow, moorhen,

and all those feathered others —
cousins, sisters, brothers —

who share with us here
our precarious atmosphere,

beating its thinness till it rings
with their songs and wings.

Sing for each threatened kind
that's nested here time out of mind —

sing for the sapphire blur
of the kingfisher,

for the thrush who once lorded it
on our chestnut summit,

for the fewer sparrows brawling
under eaves and awnings,

for the bullfinch with the furnace
chest who's forsaken us,

for the grebe with the fish-hook
in its half-shut beak,

for fading lapwing and lark,
and silenced corn-crake.

Sing against birdsong's
sad diminishing.

Let that be your tune,
thing with feathers.

Sing it in all weathers.

SWALLOWS IN SEPTEMBER

Anyone would know they're going
from the way they dash in and out
of their blue rooms of air

in frantic last-minute preparation,
rushing dipping and skidding
along the river, scouring

its surfaces before turning
to come hurtling over the grass as if
searching for something forgotten.

Listening to them as they spill
scattering down from the wires,
watching them rummaging in the shadows

at the corner of a field of stubble
then cutting across the leaf-strewn paths
in a familiar unfollowable zaniness,

and thinking of them here again
next summer, it's easy to forget
how many reaches of dark sea

and hammering winds, how many freezing
nights and days of burning sun, how many
hunters' guns they'll need to survive

if they're to come back to us again.
I think there should be a ceremony
for taking leave of the swallows.

'GIFT OFFER — TRADITIONAL WISHING WELL — £47.50'

But how could anyone try to sell
this for a well?

How could anyone wish for a well
that's waterless,
with a bottom that's skyless?

How can you make a wish
with such an ill
well, an immobile one
with a handle fixed
in a timeless trance
and the rope nailed down?

A well with no chance
to creak or spill
or glint in the sun
or whisper secretly
far down,
where you can't pull
on a shiny handle
till a shivering rope
brings a nearly full
bucket up

swinging and spilling
level with you,
trembling
with reflected blue —

a well with no wall
to lean over
till you see yourself small
and far down
in a needle's eye
of blue sky —

a dust-dry well
with no moss or damp
or dripping brickwork
to smell,
no echoing dark
to drop stones into,
and count the interval
of their silent fall
to tell how far
down there
that small

splash
in the silence was.

What can you wish for
without water?

SHOPPING AT CHRISTMAS

Suppose we think of the whole thing,
however beautiful it all is —
the cards, parties, presents, food,
the jollity and crackers,
even the carol-services and nativities
and bells ringing —
as a kind of wrapping;

even the story
of three kings journeying
towards a barn
under a star's burning,
and the angels singing their dazzling news
to shepherds dozing
in frozen fields
with freezing mittened fingers,
then the breath of animals kneeling
that is soft and warm on our hands
as we reach in closer and get nearer;

suppose we think of it all
as really only the bright wrapping
that every year enthrals us,
hiding the gift
from our waiting eyes;

and suppose that shining brilliant gift
when it's unwrapped
and lies there before us
as the child Jesus
is simply love —

and suppose love
is the only gift.

THE TALE OF SIR TOBY
THE TIMID

What a great bustle
all round the castle
of Toby the Timid,
as they put up tents
and tables and benches,
and try to damp down
the ancient stenches.

And why? today —
'Oh yeah! Oh yeah!' —
is Tournament Day!
the day in the year
when all the best knights
assemble in beautiful
suits of armour
with long bright lances
on lovely horses
to ride at a clatter
and biff and batter
and bam each other —
zap dang b-doing —
slap to the floor!

And the people cheer
and shout for more.

Now poor Sir Toby's
a timid knight,
he's scared of spiders
and noises at night;
mice and hamsters
give him a fright,
and he's totally hopeless
at charging on horses
and fighting and chivalry.

But every year
he wins first prize
for being the best-
dressed, gentlest,
most courteous knight
in all the revelry.

His squires come before him,
to dress him for battle.
'Sir, here is your best
tin battle-vest,
and your underpants
with the map of France,
and your armour, scoured clean
and bright, your honour.'

Sir Toby looks cross.
'What's on earth's this?
This armour's all dented
and crumpled and battered!
I shall look a right fright
in this wonky suit
of crumply old metal!
I need it un-dented,
smooth and unrumpled
and ready for battle!'

'Your honour,
no iron or hammer
could ever smooth flat
this bashed-up old armour —
but it's tough and true
and as handsome as you.'

'Ancient men,
my battle's at ten.
If my armour isn't
flat by then
I'll jolly well rattle
your silly old heads
with your hammers and irons,
you idle villains,

and bring down a curse —
something vile or worse —
on all your relations,
so — action stations!'

'Sir Toby, sir,
we just can't hammer
an old suit of armour
completely uncrinkly
and flat!
And that's that!'

Sir Toby the Timid
grew furious and livid,
and redder and crosser
to think that the prize
for the best-dressed
most gentle knight
might not be his,
so that by the time
they called his name —
'Sir Toby the Timid!' —
to ride and clatter
with long bright lances
on lovely horses
and biff and batter

another fine knight,
so cross he was
that — *zap dang b-doing* —
he bammed first one
fine knight then another
slap whang to the floor,
and the people roared,
and shouted for more.

'Hail, Toby the Terrible!'
they shouted and roared,
and he won the prize
for the fiercest knight
on horseback in battle.

At first Sir Toby
liked his new name,
then Monday came,
and at supper he said,
'Please will you call me
'Sir Timid' again.
I like it much better
than 'Toby the Terrible'

which I think is a horrible
name to have, especially
if one's truly
a gentle knight
who's frightened of mice
and fighting and spiders
and creepy crawlies
and noises at night.'

HUMPTY, THE TRUE STORY

Humpty Dumpty sat on a wall
thinking of not very much at all

and thinking of not very much at all
Humpty Dumpty had a great fall —

zoom! — to the pavement — *whack!* — *splat!*
he lay there concussed, feeling rather flat.

Now who should be riding by just then
but all the King's horses and cleverest men,

who gazed down at Humpty and puzzled a lot
but couldn't think what to do — on the spot.

So the Captain phoned the King and Queen
and got Regal Advice. 'Look here old bean,

the Queen and I have too much to do
to be bothered with problems. It's up to you

to get rid of this creature, or face disgrace.
He must have landed from outer space,

he's an alien, we can't let him stay.
I don't know what my old dad would say.

54

If we don't watch out he'll be here for years.
So look, just round up some volunteers

and get them to put him together again.'
'Right ho,' said the Captain. 'Listen, men,

the King says to round up volunteers —
nurses, carpenters, engineers,

post-persons, jugglers, tall-crane-drivers,
footballers, vicars, deep-sea divers,

and get them all here by half-past ten,
to put this fellow together again;

then we can fire him off into space
from that launching pad at the Duke's place.

Off you go, just obey my instructions,
otherwise there'll be terrible ructions.'

The volunteers came as fast as they could.
The first was a carpenter, straight from the wood,

with an axe and chisel and shavings and glue,
and not a clue about what he could do,

then people like bakers, barbers, bankers,
pantomime horses and captains of tankers,

but all these clever women and men
just couldn't put Humpty together again.

They tried this, then that, then other things,
which would never work till pigs get wings.

Now a small girl was watching, dressed in blue.
Her name was Felicity Abigail Drew.

She'd a coloured umbrella she'd found in the pond
which she waved over Humpty just like a wand,

and — *crackle!* — all Humpty's bits shot together
like a shoal of fish or clouds in strange weather,

and — *whoosh!* — high up, on the very same wall,
as if he'd never had his great fall,

sat Humpty, all together again,
smiling down at the women and men,

and the soldiers and horses and volunteers
with the biggest smile they'd seen for years.

He waved to Felicity Abigail Drew
as she skipped off home — she'd things to do —

and all the King's horses and all the King's men
decided to trot round the town again,

while the volunteers went home for dinner,
and Humpty, a lot less shiny, and thinner,

made himself comfy sat on the wall,
thinking of not very much at all.

SHINY CHEERY POEM

The light shines bright
on Bognor prom.

It shines on the newly white
white-washed wall

and bottle-tops
stamped on the prom

and seagulls swaying
on silver-top waves.

It seethes at sea
in a mint of glitter,

it coils in the snails'
scintillant trails

on wooden seat-backs,
and celebrates

from the gleaming gables
of white-as-gulls villas.

No money won
on gaming tables

binges at Bingo
or jittery lotteries

is half the fun
by jingo

of light on the prom
full of breeze

and bounce
and tiddly pom.

HIGH TIDE

Seaside autumn —
the dodgems are in hibernation,
all the rides are ridden.

Only a few loiterers
stare from under umbrellas
at the sand that's still summer yellow
and the hard rain pimpling the harbour
and the tide turning back the river
that's rising and rising
in the harbour in the rain.

Surely the tide's high enough,
surely it's finished coming in —
when men from the last fishing-boat
churning past in the rain
can peer into the tea-shops
on the harbour-side road
and read the menus outside.

One day sometime,
on an afternoon like this,
the tide will keep rising
and rising and some of the land
will come to an end.

The corner pub will need stilts then,
the fairground will be the foreshore,
only the castle with its tower
and the high rides will be open.

That day, one of the casual loiterers
watching the rising waters
will be caught unawares
and have to scramble the crinkly slide
to the crenellated battlements
and ask one of the stiffly gleaming
chocolate box soldiers
guarding the security light
if he could shelter inside
till the next — if there is one —
ebb tide.

SEASIDE SEPTEMBER

On sandy slipways
yachts strain
under tarpaulin.

Yesterday
summer called here,
with suns that swayed

in holiday litter,
and air that quietly
did no more

than dishevel
reflections of mast
and sail.

Now autumn
edges in;
a fine rain

mists the wharves;
coils of chain
rust deeper

into each other.
By October's end
the harbour

will be the wind's
restless mooring,
then November

will bring its freight
of dark alongside,
ready for winter

to weigh anchor.

USEFUL PHRASES FOR WHEN YOU'RE ON HOLIDAY . . .

We shall climb to the top
We don't need a guide
What terrible weather
We like our eggs fried

Please say it again
Are the camels for hire?
Is this an oasis?
We've got a flat tyre

We're not in a hurry
Please go much faster
Is that a pyramid?
We prefer pasta

I don't have a spanner
a corkscrew a knife
I can't find my wallet
my passport my wife

There's dirt on the beach
We don't like the food
We can't work the shower
The waiter is rude

This camera is broken
The sunshade is ripped
Our pedalo's leaking
The tour-leader's flipped

We think we'll go home now
Is that our plane?
Oh yes it was lovely
We'd come here again

AUTUMN FLOOD

Today no cattle
go to grazing;
under the circling
cries of gull and lapwing
their pasture
flows like a river.

Today the ferry
makes no crossing;
its frail mooring
of old scaffolding
and planking
is drowning.

Today the moorhens
don't know where
they wander; the rains
have lifted them
from sunny alleys
of pottering quiet

to the blue roof
of a new river
brimming with glitter
and turbulence,

where willows
drag and drag,
offshore, in silence.

GNOME AT THE GARDEN CENTRE

'Oh for a home!'
sighed the gnome —
'nothing much,
just a grassy patch

not far from the cabbage
and rhubarb and peas,
in a space with a bit of breeze
now and then,

hopefully under some trees,
say apple or cherry,
near raspberry bushes or black
currant or gooseberry,

with bees humming round —
the sound of bees
near your home puts a gnome
at his ease.

For a social
life it's preferable
to live amongst friends —
gnomes on the same

familiar footing,
a circle of folk
with a similar outlook,
gnomes with like minds

and shared horizons.
Those are the dreams
we gnomes dream here
waiting in lines

like a chorus of clones,
the rain tumbling down,
and some of us waiting
more than a year.

Oh yes, it's a strain,
the waiting, the rain,
and the sound of being locked in
at night again.'

EVENING SONG

Shadows, lengthen
day, draw in
woodland, welcome
blackbird's hymn.

Stream, glimmer
oak, whisper
deer, fear
no trespasser.

Turn slow, night
burn clear, star
owl, call
to owl afar.

Winds, be stilled
house, be lit
love, wait
safe in it.